The fence posts had white hats.
Seth bundled up in his warm
snowsuit to go outside.

3

Step, step, step, step. Seth's feet
made a pattern in the snow.

Snow

More Complex Patterns

by Lynn Maslen Kertell
pictures by Sue Hendra and John R. Maslen

Scholastic Inc.
New York • Toronto • London • Auckland • Sydney • Mexico City • New Delhi • Hong Kong • Buenos Aires

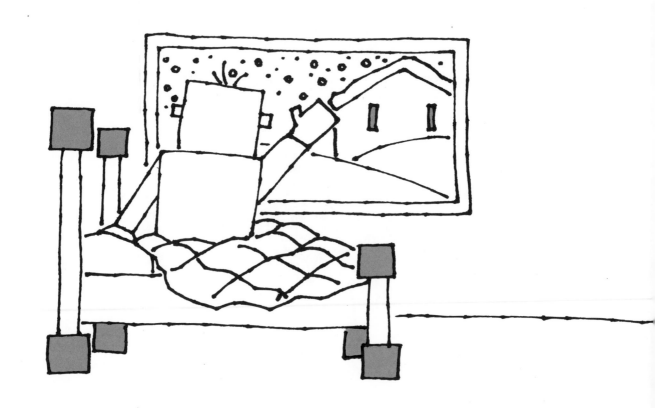

When Seth woke up, the
ground was covered with white.

Hop, hop, hop, hop. Seth could change the pattern.

Seth found a stick.
He made a new design.

Hop, drag, hop, drag.
Look at his pattern now!

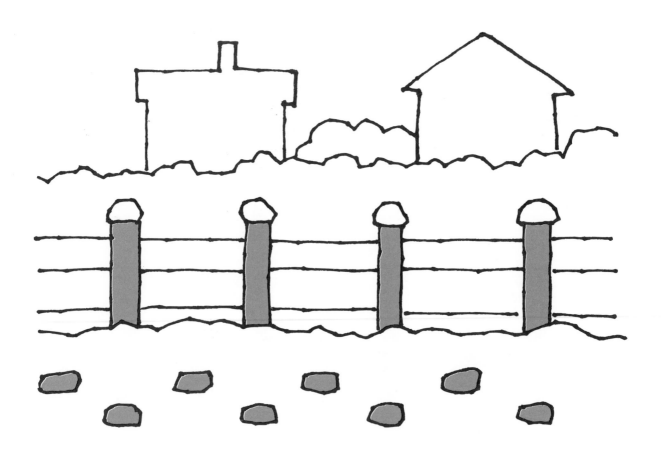

The caps of snow made
a pattern on the fence.

Whack! Seth changed the pattern!

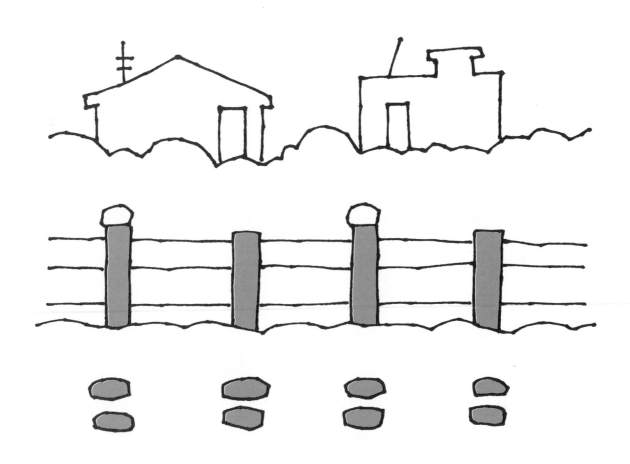

Jump, whack, jump, whack.

Jump, drag, jump, drag.

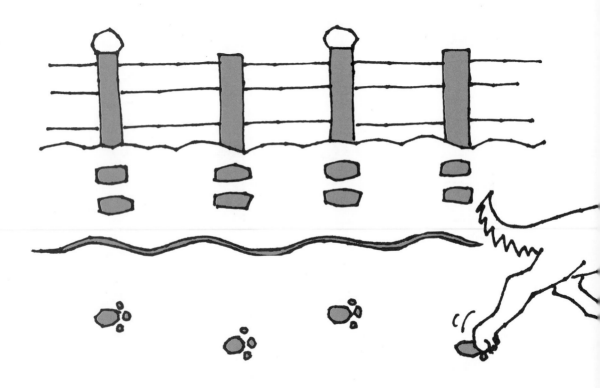

It is time to go home. Look what
Seth's dog did to his pattern!